Penelope

in Belgravia

A Pictorial Diary set in London in the Seventies

by

Edwina Sandys

Edwina Sandys

2000

Library of Congress Cataloguing-in-Publication Data
ISBN: 0-9677003-1-0

Published by: Millennium Woman
565 Broadway, #2 New York, NY 10012
(1-800-566-6630)

Illustrations & text by Edwina Sandys
www.edwinasandys.com
Design by Lauree Feldman
Printed by Dollco Printing in Canada

First Edition

in memory of
Nanny
(Miriam J. Buckles)

FOREWORD

by Sir Peregrine Worsthorne

Journalists are accustomed to writing their articles against a clatter of distractions -- in a crowded aircraft, a noisy hotel foyer, or even a slit trench. But this is by necessity rather than choice. Edwina Sandys actually prefers to paint against a background of action, as I discovered this summer while staying in her Tuscan farmhouse outside Lucca where some of the most delectable of these paintings were done.

Let me paint my picture of the scene -- a crowd of talkative guests around the swimming pool, some noisily in, some equally noisy out; Edwina on the terrace just below, drops of water still glistening on her back, canvas propped up on a chair, painting away to the sound of Ludwig van on the radio, interrupting her brush-strokes to greet a new arrival, to explain how the coffee machine works, to instruct on and demonstrate the skills of swallow-diving, to mix a drink or treat a horsefly bite, always returning, however, to the painting in hand with ever mounting enthusiasm, her artistic inspiration seemingly augmented and fortified by all the chores and distractions of ordinary life.

Not for her the seclusion of the studio or the dreadful loneliness of the creative process. Her art is essentially and gloriously part of ordinary living, the paint flowing like conversation, or rather between bouts of conversation, with the canvases somehow materializing, along with the meals and the witticisms, colourful, bursting with idiosyncratic verve, not as something separate and distinct from the business of living, but as an extension of it. Few paintings that I know are such good company as Edwina's are. Having one on the wall is like having her presence in the room. They radiate her personality as a rose spreads its scent. Her voice speaks from the canvas as if on tape.

I do not know whether this is high art. It is not for me to judge, since I am no critic. But it is certainly high visual journalism, since the pictures capture attention at first glance, and hold it too, until every detail has been examined, the curiosity growing with what it feeds on.

That pair of boots, that bottle of whisky -- they all seem to have a life of their own, a story to tell, a secret to disclose, or a joke to recount, quite as much as the people portrayed. In Edwina's painting there is nothing which could conceivably be described as an inanimate object. Within them all there seems to be some sprite or imp trying to escape. Of one thing I am certain -- Edwina's studies, most emphatically, are not 'still lives', not *nature morte*.

Has anyone ever seen tulips which wave at one with such languorous longing, or chairs that challenge one to sit on them with such cheerful audacity, or jugs that positively wink at one with such alcoholic complicity, or banana skins which have such a look of sad dejection? And as for humans, where better than in her paintings does the face of a child suggest so movingly all the sorrows and joys of the future?

Perhaps I am waxing too lyrical. Of course Edwina is a friend. Love me, love my paintings. There must be a bit of that. But I do find them irresistible. They have given me true delight, as much in their making -- watching Edwina work, or is it play? -- as when they are finished on the wall. Bewitching, is that the right word? As true of the art as of the artist.

Servente, Tuscany, September 1973

THE WAY WE WERE

Preface by Edwina Sandys

This story, told in pictures and words,
describes the personal world of Penelope,
a fictitious 33 year-old woman living in
Belgravia in the early Seventies.

Using paintings I made in London thirty
years ago to jog my memory, I have now
added words to these images to create this
book. Daydreaming back to those vivid,
and seemingly carefree days, I let myself go
-- trying to become the people we were and
knew -- to think and talk the way we did.

The early Seventies were a strange time --a crossover time. Questions were raised
and few answers were found. Brought up in one world and on the cusp of another,
Penelope is hardly aware the world is changing. A blithe spirit in tune with the
Sixties, by the Seventies her world has lost the blithe and caught the blahs.

Looking back across the gulf of three decades, Penelope, in her privileged world,
seems frivolous and snobbish. A generation before Sloanes, she was too young to
have been part of the Chelsea Set. She just missed being a hippy and smoking pot.
She was already married by the time the full impact of the Permissive Society was
felt. Only vaguely aware of Womens' Lib, she hardly knew there was anymore to
it than burning bras.

Married in white, almost a virgin at twenty-three, Penelope settled into the life
that was expected of her. Get married, do up a house, have two babies, move
house -- then what?

Inevitably, there's something of me in Penelope and something of Penelope in me. I went to school with Penelopes, I went to the Pony Club with Penelopes, I danced with Penelopes' brothers. Penelope married Tony, who was the male equivalent of herself. For some reason, I resisted being a total Penelope.

Part of the fun of putting this book together is remembering the happy times when I first took brush to canvas. My first and foremost model was Ann-Mari McDougall, whose expressive features and amenable disposition inspired the major part of my early paintings. While her children and mine were playing upstairs, we would sit in her kitchen in Wilton Street for hours on end, she smoking a cigarette, me sucking a Magic Marker. "Go on, Ann-Mari," I would entreat her. "Make a sad/happy/angry face, turn this way, look that way! Take your clothes off/put them on!" Everything in her house and mine was put to good use -- flower pots, curtains, teapots, bookshelves, old shoes, new dresses -- and, of course, the children, who posed, more or less patiently, as I explored my new-found world of images.

In the Seventies, newly divorced, I lived at 66 Chester Row with Nanny and the boys. Mark and Hugo were my best friends and my fiercest critics. Friends

coming to our house would be given a drink, sat down in a chair and told not to move a muscle until I had got them down on my sketch pad. Using these sketches, I would juxtapose people who had never met, placing them in imaginary and sometimes intimate situations.

I thank my family and all the friends who have encouraged me over the years, and especially my husband, Richard Kaplan.

I thank the late Charles Ross, who gave me my very first show, at "The Spot" restaurant in the King's Road, and Andras Kalman [pictured above], who launched me on an unexpected but thrilling career in Art. Last, but certainly not least, a big "thank you" to those who not only bought my paintings, but who -- to my mind almost a greater compliment -- gave them hanging room.

New York City, 2000

Penelope

in Belgravia

BREAKFAST IN BED

"...if I have a ghost, this is where it would live..."

I've had breakfast in bed almost every day since Tony and I were married ten years ago. Breakfast time is almost my favourite time of the day and bed is certainly my favourite place. I love having meals in bed. Tony hates it -- most men do. I read in bed. I write letters in bed. I do the household accounts, play games with the children, plan the day with Nanny, talk to my friends on the telephone, and receive visitors in or on bed. If I have a ghost, this is where it would live -- propped up on pillows, my side of the bed.

The blue envelope was lined with pink, a little brighter than Tony's Financial Times. I wish he wouldn't leave his paper on the quilted bedspread I just got from Peter Jones to match the headboard. It's only The Times that has that really good quality paper, the sort the ink doesn't come off. I put the handwritten letter back in its envelope. The colour and style looked as if it was from a woman but I recognized John's handwriting. I'd read it later when Tony was out of the house.

Nanny's coffee was delicious this morning, just right, with hot milk, which makes all the difference. I've given up eggs and bacon and feel very virtuous crunching a slimming, sparsely covered ryvita, with marge and only a smattering of dark Oxford marmalade. No sugar for me,either. Tony should really give it up, too.

SHAVING

"...the ideal man would be Tony and John rolled into one..."

He pulled the skin taut with his left hand and made the first furrows through the shaving cream. Like tracks through new snow. Whoops! Just for the moment before it cakes up and turns dark, new blood is such a beautiful clear red. The same colour as the towels and the tulips -- my favourite flower.

Women liked him. So did I, basically, even after ten years. But, lately, we were not quite so close. Nothing specific, at least nothing I could put my finger on. Like the "his and hers" toothbrushes teetering on the edge of the wash-basin, we were facing opposite directions. The gold taps seemed more friendly -- the way we used to be. Before I started meeting John. John was the opposite of Tony. The ideal man would be Tony and John rolled into one.

An early start is essential for the man in my life. Something in my upbringing makes me feel guilty if I get going before he does. I must lie back in bed and patiently look at his back while he shaves and fusses around. The minute I hear the front door bang, I'm galvanized into action. I reach for the telephone and speak to the outside world. If, for any reason Tony returns, he finds a very different me. When he malingers at home with a cold, I might as well turn my energy down to low and write the day off. I have great admiration, but not envy, for Continental women, whose husbands not only care what they eat, but who also come home to lunch every day.

Maybe I would read the letter after all. In the gilt mirror, Tony's eye caught mine, and I decided against it. He wiped off the spot of blood.

NANNY

"...there's no television in the house except in Nanny's room..."

Like any child with a parent, I take Nanny for granted -- the only person who's lived with me all my life. In all my thirty-three years, I lived with my parents for less than twenty of them. Nanny was there before I was born and, when I married Tony, she moved in with us as soon as I was pregnant with Melissa. Nanny has always meant "home" to me although now, I also mean home to her.

There's no television in the house except in Nanny's room, where the children and Tony and I crowd in when there's anything on -- "Upstairs & Downstairs", and the Queen's broadcast on Christmas Day.

The eldest of thirteen, Nanny was born in 1900, in Queen Victoria's reign. She gave me a sepia photograph of herself at ten, a serious Alice-in-Wonderland in

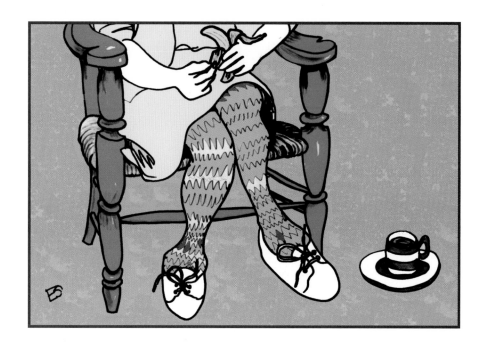

high button boots. She loves to reminisce about her childhood - "No hoover, no radio, no fridge. The milkman walked his cow to the back door and milked her right there, filling up our own jugs with hot frothy milk, then the pair of them would move on down the street to the next house."

She never married. "I've seen enough of men and the things that go on." She was a hospital nurse at the end of the First World War, and then had a series of jobs as a children's nanny -- getting turfed out when her charges reached the age of seven or eight -- each time breaking her heart -- and theirs. Finally, she got stuck in our family and, like Ponds lipstick, stayed on and on.

In those days Nanny only got wages of a measly £3 a week. I swore, when I grew up I would make it up to her, so Tony and I give her £2 over the going rate. Not that she has extravagant tastes. All her clothes are Navy blue and, Winter or Summer, her Arthritis legs are always encased in thick, ribbed, lisle stockings -- the same colour as the sweet, milky tea she's addicted to.

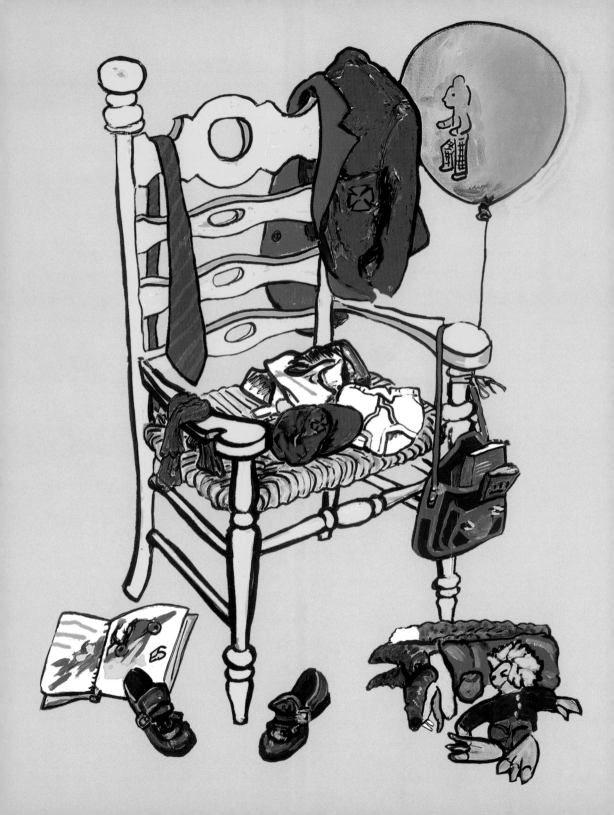

RUPERT'S CLOTHES

"...he wants to relive his school days through Rupert..."

School uniforms look so sweet to parents, as do the schools themselves. Rupert's "baby" school, Eton House, really is quite nice and gentle. Wait until he goes to his "prep" school! I dread to think of him going away from home at only seven and a half. Tony's mad keen on it. He wants to relive his schooldays through Rupert, but do it better. I can usually get my way on most things in our marriage, but on this subject I have no say. "Let's face it, Pen," Tony said " You haven't a clue about boys'. I'll decide about Rupe and leave you a free hand with Melissa."

BASIL BRUSH

"...he won't be able to take his soft toys..."

Rupert hasn't any idea what's in store for him at boarding school. Tony's led him to believe it'll be like staying with his cousins in Hampshire -- ponies, fishing, and midnight feasts. He won't be able to take his soft toys with him. Since he was two, he hasn't slept a night without Basil Brush curled beside him. And, lately, the two of them have been making quite a nuisance of themselves. Last week, he put his beloved glove puppet over a broom handle, and climbing up the sycamore tree by the garden wall, managed to reach the window at the half-landing of the house next door. Lady Standish was on the loo when she caught sight of a toothy foxface leering at her. Nanny, had heard this from the Standish cook. I confiscated Basil for a week, but Nanny and I had a good giggle about it when Rupert was in bed.

FORMER BEAUTY

"...it's no longer cutlet for cutlet..."

I hate to think of Mother living in reduced circumstances. Of course, Tony and I help her as much as we can, but accepting charity from the Younger Generation can be a humiliating experience. Father was quite a big shot and, when he was alive, she was at the centre of things. But, when you're a widow, you don't just lose the man, you lose his lifestyle, too - no Emperor no Empire. It's not just the money -- a flat in Cadogan Square hardly qualifies for help from The Distressed Gentlefolks Association. But she's lost her influence. She's lonely, though she rarely admits it. She says she goes out a lot, but I think she stays in many evenings, sitting on her single bed, staring into space, smoking and thinking.

It must be hard being a former beauty. She used to be "ravishing" when she was young. She even danced with the Prince of Wales the night before he met Mrs. Simpson. I'm not nearly as pretty as Mother was, so I don't depend on my looks, which should stand me in good stead in the long run.

"I have to be nicer, now, and so tolerant!" Mother confided in me. "I'm not as popular nowadays. It's no longer cutlet for cutlet. I ask people for dinner, they ask me back for cocktails."

In my opinion, she's drinking too much. Oh, she never drinks much in front of other people, even Tony and me. "Just a light, very light, whisky and soda." But I think she stokes up at home before she goes out. There's something rather pathetic about an older woman drinking. Why is it alright for an older man?

THE LETTER

"...sometimes he would write a whole letter in hieroglyphics..."

Dearest Penelope,
I saw you last night, but you didn't see me... you were wearing the leather suit --and smelling of Fracas. I was invisible...

Where had I been last night? At whose party? I hadn't seen John.
I ran through the evening -- I met Tony at 6.30 at the Phillipses -- they're awfully nice but a little on the square side. Then the four of us had walked over to see the Harold Pinter play at the Royal Court Theatre.

But, where was John? Was he that awful old man in the beard and glasses, who kept his gloves on during the whole performance. Could it have been John who kept dropping his programme on the floor and breathing heavily down my neck as he bent to pick it up? I should have been revolted, but I had felt a strange magnetism and had been aware of his every move.

You were loving the play. It didn't hold my attention, but then I was concentrating on my own performance. Penelope, I am longing to...

I wanted to savour the moment before turning the page and finding out how he would end. That was the delightful thing about John. He always surprised you. Would there be a line from Shakespeare, a sly sensual suggestion, or an adorable sketch? Sometimes he would write a whole letter in Hieroglyphics.

I decided to tease myself and wait until after lunch. I folded the letter carefully and put it inside the pages of *Les Liaisons Dangereuses*, putting it back in the bookcase between *Anna Karenina* and *Couples*.

SHAMPOO

"...with my head under the tap, my mind wanders freely..."

I used to go to the hairdresser twice a week and more often when there were lots of dances. It's impossible to park these days. The meter maids give you a ticket if you so much as slow down in the vicinity of Harrods. I wash my hair myself, now -- except when Bruno comes to do me at home, which is heaven.

With my head under the tap, my mind wanders freely. It must be something to do with the blood rushing to your head and seeing the world upside down. Proust was quite right about the Madeleines. It's amazing how the tiniest thing can trigger off crystal clear images of the past. The sound of water sluishing through my hair and the smell of Vidal's almond rinse transports me to warm places.

Ten years ago, Tony and I spent our honeymoon in Mykonos in an incredibly simple, white-washed cottage. Absolutely no mod. cons. We couldn't stand the wine -- mouthwash. But we loved the food, and the music. *Never on a Sunday* became "our song".

We met Laszlo playing backgammon on the beach, and we discovered he knew everyone we knew. He took us under his wing. It was utter bliss. We had dinner, one evening, in the Square with a big ship owner. His brother-in-law was giving a rival party on his yacht. That famous actress, the one they all think is so beautiful but I think is hideous, was invited to both, so she had to be ferried back and forth all night long.

Apparently, now, according to Mother's decorator, Mr. Cornice, the island has changed a lot. The hairdressers have discovered it and the ship owners barely come ashore. I must tell Bruno -- though, come to think of it, I suppose he knows.

THE GAME
"... his only visible means of support..."

Laszlo is a Hungarian Baron. "That's *his* story," says Nanny. "Titles are two a penny on the Continent." She may be right. Sometimes I've wondered myself. But I wouldn't really want to catch him out. He'd be left with nothing. I do know for a fact that during the Hungarian Revolution he only got as far as the Hotel Bristol in Vienna. A bit humiliating since Tony's older brother and some of his friends did reach Budapest, and helped dozens of refugees over the border.

Laszlo's always very prompt, even early for parties, and, at the last cocktail we gave, he'd already taken ten quid off the temporary butler at backgammon before any of the guests arrived. "Carstairs wanted to learn -- so I taught him the hard way." explained Laszlo, with a twitch of his lips. "It's really bad form," said Tony afterwards, " but you have to forgive him. He needs the money, and he's so charming."

Tcharrming he is -- especially to the ladies. He'll play games with ladies of any age, shape, or denomination. When it comes to playing games with a man, there are some advantages in being a woman. You're not expected to win, so if you do, you're brilliant and, if you lose, you may win other things. And some men, patronizingly, let a woman win. Not Laszlo.

Gambling is the love of his life and Backgammon his particular thing. It's also his profession -- his only visible means of support. Generally, he gives the appearance of being a rather flimsy person, but there's steel in him when he sits down to play. I've never seen anyone concentrate so hard. While weighing the odds, I truly believe, he wouldn't notice if a naked girl walked past his nose.

WINDOW SHOPPING

"...this is for you, Tony, I breathed..."

Sometimes I feel like doing something really outrageous -- before I'm too old, over the hill. Happily, in my mind, the hill keeps receding. I remember mourning my youth on my twenty-fifth birthday.

I dare myself to do things, to show myself I'm still alive. Yesterday, I was window shopping in Jermyn Street. It was drizzling, and I stopped in front of T& A's window, which always makes me want to be a man. Such a glorious display of shirts and ties, hats and belts! The blue and grey striped shirt would suit Tony, or maybe even the solid pink. I'd love to give the green one to John. Imagine if all the shirts were filled with men -- of all shapes and sizes?

I wiggled my bottom a little -- half a wiggle, half a dance. With my hands sunk into my pockets, and, concentrating hard on the blue and grey shirt, I flashed open my mackintosh. This is for you, Tony," I breathed. Then at the green shirt. "For you, John." Then at the yellow, the red, and the ruffled dinner shirt. "For you, for you, and for you! For Martin, my first boyfriend, for all the men everywhere, for all the men who've ever lived and who will live." I was working up quite a religious fervour, and making quite a wind, flapping my raincoat back and forth. I half expected the shirts to come alive and start singing the Hallelujah Chorus.

"Good afternoon, Mrs. Barrington. It is Penelope Barrington, isn't it?" The stentorian voice behind me brought me down to earth like a collapsed souffle. I turned round, simultaneously folding my coat in front of me like a pair of bat's wings, coming face to face with the Rector of St. James's.

"Are you quite well, my dear?" he enquired, his kindly hand on my shoulder. "Just a little warm, Rector," I panted. "The weather's turned and I've still got the fur lining in my Burberry."

MUMMY'S CLOTHES

"...there's something very contrary about Melissa..."

No matter what some people like to think, physically and mentally, inside and out, girls *are* different from boys. Just as cows are different from bulls. Nobody's frightened of going into a field full of cows, but a single bull.... Everyone agrees that the packaging is different, so why do they expect the contents to be the same?

My little Melissa is every inch a feminine creature, though sometimes she tries to disguise it, since she's noticed that boys travel First Class through life. She loves dressing up in my clothes. She will come in from the garden, throw off her filthy old denim shorts and jumper, fling her toys on the floor and try on every dress in my wardrobe. Hobbling around in my wedge-heeled shoes, she will prink and preen in front of the mirror for hours.

I didn't have fun like this with my parents when I was seven. In fact, I didn't have fun with them at all until after I was grown up. Tony and I made a pact when we got married -- that we'd be friends with our children if we did nothing else. Perhaps we overdo it. We have no locks on the bathroom doors and the children can come into our bedroom almost any time. On special occasions like birthdays and Christmas, we all four crowd in together to have breakfast in bed with Nanny looking on, perched on the little stocking chair. I suppose there'll come a time when this'll have to stop -- unless we acquire the Great Bed of Ware!

There's something very contrary about Melissa. She has the loveliest clothes of her own, including a party frock from Paris. She parades throughout the house in them, showing off. But when she's invited to a party, will she ever, I mean ever, wear them? We were all dressed up, in the taxi, just leaving with Mother for the Mansion House children's party last week, when, at the last minute, Melissa dashed back into the house and returned wearing smelly jeans and sandals.

PLAYTIME

"...they call it the Permissive society on Telly..."

Patrick and Henrietta are both Pisces and spend a lot of time in the bath. They have a gorgeous bathroom with paintings and sculptures in alcoves. Henrietta did it up with tiles from Positano. It's the best room in the house. They have a tray that fits over the bath for cocktails or to play cards, while soaking in bubblebath.

Nanny doesn't approve of Patrick and Henrietta. Although Henrietta, who tries to look like Sophia Loren, is Melissa's godmother, and gives her super presents. "*He*'s all right, but there's something about *her* I can't abide," said Nanny. "They call it the Permissive Society on Telly but I call it playing fast and loose."

"Whatever do you mean, Nanny?" I questioned. "I hear things, from the other Nannies - in the park." "What things?" I asked. "Never you mind." She clamped her lips and would not be drawn.

Last Summer, Patrick and Henrietta spent a week on that nudist island in the South of France. It's quite fashionable. You only meet nice people there. There's a good hotel, a bit like a club. Evenings are quite formal -- cocktails on the terrace at seven, seated dinner at eight -- all without a stitch on. Oh, the men can wear ties, and the women jewelry. Then dancing. Imagine dancing the Bossa Nova with a naked stranger - the mind boggles.

They even took the children! -- that must be what Nanny was going on about.. They're going again this year and have invited us. I would secretly rather like to go but Tony pooh-poohed it immediately. "I'd have to wear a shirt so as not to get sunburnt, so what's the point?" he joked. "We'll go to St. Tropez as usual and the birds can go topless on the Pamplonne Beach." That's all very well for the men, but what do *we* get out of it, other than toasted tits?"

MONOPOLY

"...but, since the Arab invasion, prices have sky rocketed..."

House hunting with Mother is a fruitless operation. She can't get used to living in a flat. "I like to be on 'terra firma', to have some sort of a garden even if it's the size of a pocket handkerchief," she sighed.

But, since the Arab invasion, prices have sky rocketed. They are buying up all the best parts of London. It seems to have happened overnight. Suddenly, characters wearing robes and veils are intermingled with ordinary shoppers. Harrods, where we collapsed for tea, has become the new Mecca. "They ought to rename is 'Harrabs'," quipped Mother, as we struggled through the China Department. I shuddered at the garish, over-sized and over-gilded jars and ornaments, shamelessly aimed at the bulging Arab pocket.

Miles and Sandra called with an SOS last night. Tony and I had to drop everything and rush over to their house for dinner -- to help entertain some important Arab clients who had descended upon them at the last minute.

"Get dressed quickly! We can't let them down," said Tony, changing back into his business suit. We both pitied Miles. In his business, he's at the beck and call of two or three wealthy Arabs. Miles is expected, at any time of the day or night, to find doctors for sick mothers, schools for numerous children and hotel rooms for equally numerous wives and concubines. All this has to be personally supervised by Miles. He does more for them than he does for his own family, which makes Sandra cross. He is also responsible for providing blondes, which makes Sandra worried.

'When in Rome' is evidently an addendum to the Koran. They may be strictly 'tea' total in the desert, but they drink like fishes in London. Miles's cellar has been completely cleaned out, including the pipe of port laid down for him at birth by his godfather, which was just getting to its peak.

We rushed over to find their Royal Highnesses had already eaten in their rooms at the Dorchester, so Sandra's lovely Coronation Chicken stayed untouched on the sideboard. The men played Monopoly, while we women pretended to look on admiringly.

DAYDREAM

"...I take all my clothes off and sort of luxuriate..."

Sometimes,when I'm alone in the house, I go into the study and turn all the blow heaters on high. I take all my clothes off and sort of luxuriate on the daybed. I lie on top of the tartan rug, but I keep a bath towel handy, just in case someone comes back home unexpectedly.

I'm not a nudist like Henrietta, but I do have a fairly decent body, and being naked is like being really alone. And a bit of a challenge. If you can be confident in yourself with no clothes on, you can build an inner strength that should get you through almost anything. At least, that's according to Darlene, my new American friend, who is a leading proponent of *Pahzitiv Thinking*.

I like daydreaming. I close my eyes and play the "what if" game. You pick a point in your life, change it and see what happens. "What if I had gone to a different boarding school, which played Hockey instead of Lacrosse, then I wouldn't have been vice-captain of the team and best friends with Caroline -- and Caroline's brother, Martin, wouldn't have invited me to the May Ball at Oxford -- then, I wouldn't have married Tony, Martin's best friend." and so on and so on "and I wouldn't have had Rupert and Melissa --I'd have had different children. Maybe some foreigner's children? How would they have looked?"

Sometimes I close my eyes very tight, and imagine that when I open them, I'll see a complete stranger looking at me through the window.

ST. JAMES'S PARK

*"...the pelicans still sun themselves on the rock
in the middle of the lake..."*

Every time I take the children to St. James's Park, memories of my own childhood come flooding back. Mother was a fresh air fiend, at least where the children were concerned. She would spend hours listening to records on the wind-up gramophone while Nanny took us for walks. Twice daily at weekends and holidays was the rule. On rainy days, dressed like Christopher Robin in our Wellington boots and Mac hats, we would traipse through the Natural History Museum. Occasionally, we took the tube to Baker Street and went downstairs at Madame Tussaud's, to the stuffy and crowded Chamber of Horrors, where Mother worried we would catch germs.

It was always the same routine -- St. James's Park in the morning and the Embankment Gardens in the afternoon. Although the Park was much more beautiful, we enjoyed "Banky" Gardens much more. A great favourite with Nanny, who had lived through the "votes for women" days, was the statue of the first suffragette, Emily Pankhurst, on the site where she chained herself to the railings by the Houses of Parliament. The Gardens are smallish and enclosed, so we were free to play as we liked. We didn't have to hold onto Nanny's hand or walk by the pram all the time.

During the war, barrage balloons were tethered in the Gardens to discourage German planes from flying along the Thames to bomb the M.P.s. Some children were sent off to safe places like Canada, or evacuated to the seaside. Father felt that was cowardly, so we stayed in London throughout the Blitz. Instead of searching for sea-shells on the beach, we collected shrapnel in the Park.

St .James's Park is still as lovely as ever -- all green and glistening.The pelicans still sun themselves on the rock in the middle of the lake. Only, today, the tower of the Hilton Hotel looms over the trees, and lovers cavort openly on the grass.

JUSTIN DE BLANK'S

"...like blood brothers we have an inherent loyalty..."

Philippa and I have lunch at least once a week, and on Nanny's day off I take the children round there to tea. While they play upstairs, she and I have heart-to-heart conversations, sitting on the banquette drinking endless cups of coffee, watching her fuss around in her kitchen.

Philippa spends ages preparing meals, even though she doesn't have a husband to worry about. She's addicted to her Kenwood mixer and even makes home-made soup and mayonnaise, which I think is a pure waste of time. You can get almost anything you want in the Food Hall at Harrods, or at Justin de Blank's and, when I decant it into my Herend dishes, no-one's any the wiser.

Philippa did one of those courses, where they teach you to make things look casual and spontaneous -- napkins that don't quite match the table-cloth, one flower a lot longer than the rest -- the by-mistake-on-purpose look. She does it with her appearance, too. She goes to the hairdresser, then comes home and messes it up.

Philippa's really my best friend -- at least my oldest friend. We were at Day School together at the age of five -- and later on at Boarding School in Kent. Like blood brothers we have an inherent loyalty. Almost stronger than family because we've chosen each other. We can talk about anything, and we do. When her husband, Dick, ran off with the Swedish Au Pair girl, Philippa telephoned at three in the morning, and I was at her house within minutes. I ended up staying five days with her, sleeping with her in the double bed, talking all night long in the dark, as if we were still in the school dorm. together.

Now, I needed someone to confide in. "I'm a bit bored with Tony," I said. "I've been thinking this for a long time, but I've never actually said it out loud"

"Noooh!" said Philippa. "You have everything I've lost, and you don't want it?"

"I didn't say I didn't want it. I know it's very spoilt of me. You envy me my security but I think your life's quite exciting."

"Not really," said Philippa, sadly, "I go out with different men all the time, but as soon as I find one I want to capture, he's off. I long to know who I'll be spending Christmas with. I get frantic when I see August looming up and there's no-one in sight."

I felt rather mean bringing my little problems up when her situation was far worse than mine. I was dying to discuss John but, clearly, this was not the moment. I'd talk it over with Henrietta, whose life at the moment is more in line with mine.

ALL DRESSED UP

"...her face, as red as the magic marker stains..."

Uncle Freddie and Aunt Pauline's 25th wedding anniversary dance was a glorious affair. As one of the top lawyers in the country, as well as being an MP, Uncle Freddie can invite anyone he pleases -- and anyone he pleases is pleased to accept. He's written books on crime and punishment, so there were people from the publishing world as well as the usual mixture of lawyers and politicians. Then there were some family. "If we ask all Freddie's and my relations, there will be no room for anyone else," Aunt Pauline put it. "Weddings, christenings, funerals, that's surely enough. Freddie and I are only inviting family whom we would choose as friends, even if they were not related."

I took a lot of trouble with my appearance. I tried out a new thing with the eyeliner, putting black under my eyes as well as on the lids. Tony wasn't sure if he liked it, but I hadn't really done it for him. I knew John would be there, invited by Philippa at my suggestion.

Before going out I went upstairs to show myself off to the children in my new Belinda Belville evening dress. I was twirling around when Nanny noticed something on the back of the ice blue, taffeta skirt. Melissa cowered behind Nanny, her face as red as the magic marker stains.

"Hold your bag over it until they've drunk enough champagne not to notice anything," was Nanny's exasperating suggestion. Swearing out loud, I grabbed the first dress I could lay my hands on -- a striped cotton with leg-of-mutton sleeves -- definitely under dressed, but Tony was waiting for me in the Jag.

BROMPTON SQUARE

"...the party was already in full swing..."

Aunt Pauline had invited the guests to Brompton Square for cocktails at eight.
When Tony and I arrived, the party was already in full swing. The L-shaped
drawing-room on the first floor was brimming with laughter and champagne.
Uncle Freddie had had the whole floor done up for Aunt Pauline as an anniversary
present. Mr. Cornice had surpassed himself. He had lined the walls and the arches
behind the bookshelves with grasspaper, imported from Hong Kong, and dyed
scarlet by a special process in Paris. Not to be outdone, the women competed for
attention in their most colourful dresses. Mr. Cornice along with some of the
younger men were wearing white silk jersey polo necks, whereas the American
contingent tended towards shirts with frills and velvet dinner jackets. Tony, and
all the really good men, were in normal black tie.

Tony charged into the fray, but I held back for a moment, surveying the scene.
I wanted to inhale the whole atmosphere before getting dug in to individual
conversations. Amongst the mostly familiar faces I noticed a sprinkling of
exciting looking strangers, hand-picked by Aunt Pauline to make the party go.

At nine o'clock a gong was sounded, and we all went next door, into the
Brammerton's old house, which is for sale and still empty. Dinner was on three
floors. Once again, Mr.Cornice had outdone himself. Ordinary trestle tables were
covered in yards of red and white regency striped silk. The tables were set up in
squares with the space inside filled with sculptures of bulls, surrounded by masses
of rhododendrons which Aunt Pauline had brought up from the country. Philippa
and I had done the arrangements. The flowers alone would have cost the earth at
Pulbrook and Gould.

PARTY

"...you'd think Cindy would die of embarrassment..."

There were a hundred dinner guests -- all seated. (Lesser mortals were invited after ten.) The 'placement' was murder for Aunt Pauline. Lord P., who was to be on her left, dropped out at lunchtime on the day itself, causing a domino effect entailing a dozen changes right down to "below the salt", where the younger generation was seated. There was a noticeable gap where Cousin Felicity should have been sitting with her dreadful rock star boyfriend.

At 10.30 we were all surprised by a loud crackle and a giant flare. We crowded the windows and balconies overlooking the garden -- some people went onto the roof -- to see a short but fabulous firework display. "Really super," exuded Cindy Raltston's stockbroker boyfriend. "Done by the chaps who do the Fourth of June. Really super!" That man is *so* proud of having been to Eton, he can't bear to go anywhere without his O.E. tie. He's had one made up as a bow tie so he can wear it with his dinner jacket. You'd think Cindy would die of embarrassment.

Then we all went back to Aunt Pauline's house for dancing. One of those pretty DJs from Annabel's was doing the disco with a complete range of songs from the last twenty-five years. Uncle Freddie's contemporaries were wonderful at the quickstep, but hopeless at anything after the Twist. Somebody turned the lights off during *Strangers in the Night* and I wondered who John was dancing with.

Actually, I was a bit fed up with John because he and Philippa, who looked quite radiant, seemed to be having such a good time. He only danced with me once -- and that was one of those jiggling dances, with no opportunity to get close. When I managed to get a word of complaint in his ear, he said he didn't want to annoy Tony.

FELICITY

"...I snatched the least dressy coat I could find..."

I noticed Aunt Pauline being dragged off the dance floor by the waiter from Brackenbury Catering. The poor fellow must have needed some nerve to delve into the darkened room and prise the imperious hostess from the arms of the Greek Ambassador to take a telephone call from the Police.

Felicity, my nineteen-year-old cousin who had not shown up at dinner, was being held on drug charges at the Police Station. I volunteered to go to the station with Uncle Freddie so that Aunt Pauline could stay at the dance. I snatched the least dressy coat I could find amongst the piles of stoles and cloaks on Aunt Pauline's bed, and buttoned it up to cover my aquamarine necklace.

Gerald Road, with its window boxes spilling over with petunias, looked more like an exhibit in the Chelsea Flower Show than a Police Station. Top criminal prosecutors, and particularly those who took part in bringing the Great Train Robbers to book, are heroes even to the most humble policemen, so when Uncle Freddie, who had had a hand in some these high profile cases, explained who he was, Sergeant Gibson practically swooned, immediately allowing Felicity to go home -- on condition that she agreed to a weewee test, and returned the next morning to appear in court.

For a moment, Felicity, looked like refusing, which would have meant her spending the night in a cell. Her extraordinary, defiant, yellow eyes held those of her father's while no-one breathed. Felicity lowered her gaze, and started biting her fingernails. The contest was over.

Within minutes we were back at Brompton Square, re-entering through the Filipinos' entrance in the basement, so the guests wouldn't notice our absence.

AFTER THE BALL

"...the keys were lying amongst the debris..."

When I woke up the next morning, I was alone in the bed. The carriage clock on my bedside table was at half past eleven! Tony had long since departed, if indeed he had been there at all. Nanny must have kept the children from coming in to see me before going to school.

I tried to put the pieces together, as I looked at my clothes flung over the red chair. The keys to Tony's car were lying amongst the debris of the night before. And the hat? Aaahh! The little grey cells were beginning to work.

Back from the Police Station, at the dance, I'd found Tony pissed as a newt, reciting Kipling to a tarty redhead in a yellow dress and fishnet tights. "I'd better drive us home," I said sadly, thinking I didn't want to miss the rest of the party. "We can't afford to have two members of the family in jail on the same night!"

"You stay, Pen. I'll walk home." He threw me the keys.

I rushed to find John, just leaving with Philippa. "Take Tony's car home," he said. "I'll pick you up in ten minutes on "your" corner of Eaton Square."

Half an hour later John and I were speeding through Soho in his red Stag, with the top down.Wearing the black velvet hat I found under the passenger seat, tied on with a green scarf, my hair still went all over the show. I had never been to Ronnie Scotts before. We sat in the dark, in pew-like seats, drinking Glenfiddich, and John kissed me deeply as Ronnie himself took to the floor with his trumpet.

Dawn must have been breaking when I crept into the house, as I have a distinct recollection of birds singing.

DOLLING UP

"...she still uses mascara you have to spit into..."

Mother has been in much better spirits lately -- and much prettier. She spends hours on her make up. She still uses the kind of mascara you have to spit into. She has new clothes, too. She takes her old Worth dresses, worn in her 'heyday', which she could never bear to part with, and has copies run up by her 'little dressmaker in Battersea'.

She's been cagey about her movements ever since the dance. Tony and I have come to the conclusion that Mother has acquired a "beau". Either that, or she's dipping heavily into her savings.

In the last two weeks, she's been to three plays, an opening in Cork Street, something at the Festival Hall (and she 'hates' concerts), and Bruno eleven times for a 'comb out'. The source of all this information? Mrs. H, the Daily (who comes weekly) drops by for a "nice cuppa" with Nanny on her way to the Pub for a Guinness.

Who could it be? Not Philippa's father -- he's dull as ditchwater.

THE BACHELOR

"...he could have a much younger woman..."

Tony and I discovered Mother's "beau" was someone we'd known for ages. We call him 'The Bachelor', although he's had four wives -- three 'official' ones. It didn't come out until much later, but his last marriage of six years to Miranda was a fake. They came back from Sicily, saying they'd been married in a village down the hill from Taormina. "Terribly romantic!" Miranda's sister gave a lovely wedding breakfast for thirty in the Chelsea Room at the Carlton Tower. Later, long after they'd parted, everyone took it as a big joke. "Sensible solution," remarked Uncle Freddie, with a lawyer's realism. "Makes divorce much simpler."

They got presents and everything. Tony and I spent quite a time going through the recycling cupboard before choosing the pair of Waterford decanters we'd been given by Mr. Cornice for *our* wedding. Useless objects! Hardly anyone uses them now, wine flows so quickly. Tony only uses decanters for plonk. "When the wine's good, I like people to see the label."

Apart from being a first rate clarinet player, the Bachelor's a gynecologist, or used to be, until he was struck off the register for seducing one of his patients. Actually, he was allowed to 'retire'. The husband was livid, but agreed not to press charges -- for the baby's sake. She was already pregnant -- that's how they met!

I have funny feelings about the Bachelor and Mother. On the one hand, he's giving her 'the rush' and she may get hurt. On the other, it may last, which would be thrilling. For her, yes, but why do I have little tweaks of jealousy or is it envy? I always thought the Bachelor had a soft spot for me. He's sixty-one now, with a wonderful 'lived in' face, only four years older than Mother, but he could have a much younger woman. Let's face it, men always can. So what does a 'Gynae' do with my Mother? What *do* older people do anyway? I mean, *do* they?

BROWNED OFF

"...I didn't want to be jollied out of my black humour..."

I've been in a bad mood all day. "Got the pip?" asked Nanny, irritatingly. The children noticed it, too. Melissa called me 'witchy', which is guarantied to put my back up. Rupert, little angel, crept up behind the long sofa and sat one of his toys over the curved back. "So you won't be lonely, Mummy," he whispered, retreating invisibly. I almost smiled, but I didn't want to be jollied out of my black humour until I'd wallowed in it for a while.

I find, if I can pin-point the reasons behind my moods, they vanish swiftly. If I cellotape over them, they lurk somewhere below the surface, ready to churn me up at the slightest invitation. There was no question about it, I was narked at Tony for bringing his new secretary back for supper last night. Not that I dislike Amanda. You couldn't really -- apart from her dreadful habit of chainsmoking. She's bright and pretty, and good listener, too. She hung on Tony's every word about his army escapades in Germany. I'd heard the stories before, and was forced to listen to them all over again, with a polite smile on my face.

ENNUI

"...I've just got my figure under control..."

I think I know what's really making me feel dreary, and it keeps returning. What is the purpose of my life? Thank God for the children. If I wake up in the middle of the night with this question, I know *they* need me -- for the next few years, anyway. And Tony? Need is too strong a word. Apart from my role as a mother -- and that I share with Nanny, who does all the real work -- of what use am I?

This sort of thing never used to enter my head. I left school, got married, did up a house, had two children, did up another house. Did all these things automatically. But I can't have more babies and do up more houses just to keep myself busy. Tony did ask me the other day if I would like to have any more nippers. I don't really think so. I've just got my figure under control and can look good in a bikini again.

What have I to look forward to in the future? More of the same? I do crave something. An interest of some sort. A job? But what could I do? Five "O" levels and a finishing school in Paris doesn't exactly train you for anything. Maybe a lover? Henrietta has two or three.

THE HUMAN ZOO

*"...I took the children to the zoo. Where they saw the animals,
I saw my friends behind the bars..."*

MORNING AFTER

"...I felt I was dickering at the edge of the diving board..."

I blew hot air on the silver frame and buffed it up with the hem of my skirt.
I lay on the bed staring at Tony's face in our black and white wedding photograph.
His well-cut profile was bent lovingly over my upturned one. From inside the
back of my Asprey's diary, I withdrew a coloured photo of John.

So clever of him to rig up a tripod and photograph himself in his green spotted
dressing gown, reading the book I'd given him for his birthday. (John is totally
anti-establishment and thinks all bankers and politicians are crooked.)
I compared the two images.

John would be handsome, too, if it weren't for his dome-shaped bald head.
Strange for a man of twenty-nine -- but, like Kojak, attractive in a way. Did I
really want John as a lover? I was definitely flattered that a man, four years
younger than me would be so keen. I felt I was dickering at the edge of the
diving board. Nanny would say what I needed was a good push. But not, of
course, if she knew what I might be getting into.

I tried to imagine what it would be like waking up, dishevelled, after a night of
passionate love, peeping out from under the bedspread -- seeing my lover's
slender waist instead of my husband's more muscled one.

What would Tony think? Would he mind? Would he even know? Maybe I should
see Darlene's psychiatrist? I heard Tony's key in the front door. Carefully, so as
not to scuff my scarlet nail polish, I slid aside the brass catch at the back of the
frame and slipped John's photograph behind that of Tony.

I ran myself a pine-scented bath.

FOOD FOR THOUGHT

"...there's no guilt since it's all agreed in advance..."

Henrietta thinks I'm unbelievably old-fashioned, not having an actual affair with John. "It's not fair on him either," she protested. "He'll find someone else who will. You'll see."

Henrietta has an open marriage with Patrick, and they both jump in and out of bed with anyone at the drop of a hat. No wonder Nanny disapproves. Henrietta says there's no guilt since it's all agreed in advance.

"You'll regret it, Penelope, when you're older," she warned me. We were sharing a lobster at Meridiana, her hang-out in the Fulham road. She's there two or three times a day, and uses the restaurant as a sort of club-cum-office. "Patrick has his office, and his Club!" she said. Their house, in Chiswick Mall, is beautiful but, as far as Henrietta's concerned, in the back of beyond.

"I bet he does. They all do anyway."

"Who does? What?" I asked, biting into a succulent pale orange claw.

"Tony, you idiot -- has affairs. All men do. The only difference in my case is that Patrick's honest enough to admit it and generous enough to let me do it, too."

Henrietta was brought up by her artist father who let her do whatever she wanted. My life so far had been totally conventional. A white wedding in every sense of the word. The permissive society hadn't reached my world. The year I "came out", most of the debs were very naive and "pure as the driven snow".

"I think what holds me back, Henrietta, is that Tony's really the only man I've ever had. I only half did it with Martin." I twirled my wine glass, shaking into action the last bubbles of the slightly frizzy white wine. "Sometimes, I feel it's inevitable, that I'm sitting on a time bomb. In a way, I wish I'd done more -- got it out of my system before getting married."

"You never do," she said with a wise look.

THE CONSULTATION

"...out of the corner of my eye, I saw the 'couch'..."

Totally confused by contradictory advice from Philippa and Henrietta, half seriously and half as a lark, I followed Darlene's suggestion to see a psychiatrist. Dr. Fergus Tryon was Heaven, so good looking. Darlene, who's a Southern Belle from Kentucky, loves everything super English. She chose him because he's the best non-Viennese psychiatrist in London -- probably the only one. I sat opposite him on a reproduction Chippendale chair. Out of the corner of my eye, I saw the 'couch' and did something I have rarely done since I was sixteen. I blushed.

"Now, Penelope, you probably don't believe any of this psychoanalysis nonsense." He had read my mind, which, of course, is what he's meant to do. "Don't worry, I won't put you on the couch until you're ready. Some of my patients have six or seven visits before I hypnotize them."

"Good Lord!" I exclaimed, multiplying seven times £20. The insurance wouldn't cover this and, since I hadn't told Tony about Dr. Tryon, I would be footing this bill, myself. "I hope we can get going faster than that."

"We'll get to know each other very well over the next few months or years, or as long as it takes," he continued. "I want you to keep a notebook by your bed and record your dreams the moment you wake. But I warn of a very common occurrence in my line of business. Do you know the meaning of 'transference'?"

"I think so," I replied, "It's when the patient falls in love with the doctor. Don't worry, I won't let it happen to me. It'd be far too embarrassing." "Ah!," he said, with satisfaction, as if he'd just got a hole in one. "That's what we'll be starting on -- things that make you embarrassed. For instance, when you were a child, did you ever see your father in the nude?"

I dreamt about him last night.

I was in the study, lying scantily dressed. Tiger was purring on the rug. Dr. Tryon, dressed in a loud version of Tony's chalk striped suit, and a wide, spotted tie, had his back to me and was staring out of the window. His eyes were bloodshot and he seemed upset. I love dreams where I am in two or three places at the same time, and see objects from all around. *"You know, Penelope, psychiatrists can have transferences, too. I feel a great temptation to caress you."* He ran his fingers through his glorious, blond, collar length hair. I clung to the yellow cushion as I willed him to do it. His face loomed over me now, obliterating everything except for the bookshelves and the corners of the ceiling. I felt pressure on my left knee and looked down to see a minute version of my father giving me a warning look. I tried to brush him aside, but he wouldn't be budged.* I woke up to find myself clutching a clump of Tiger's fur.

THE AFFAIR

"...the bedroom stays cool, even at siesta time..."

Three days seems so very long when it's a special three days. Every second savoured, every minute magnified.

Aunt Pauline had asked me to oversee the repairs to her house in Tuscany. Nanny said I should stay at home with my children and not go gallivanting abroad. Tony was to spend time with the "Territorials" and encouraged me to go. I asked John to come with me.

The house is a dream -- A converted granary of indeterminate age tucked into the side of a hill. Everything is terribly simple, bought locally from Signor Lenci's antique (second-hand) shop in Lucca. The bedroom, with its tiny square windows cut through very thick walls, stays cool, even at siesta time.

After a picnic of bread, cheese and olives, and lashings of vino bianco, John and I collapsed on the wrought iron bed. I played a game with the beams on the ceiling. Every time my eye caught sight of a knot in the old wood, I did something new to John.

It was absolutely amazing being with a man other than my husband -- a totally different roadmap! At my finishing school in Paris, Madame Anita, nervous that some of her girls might stray, tried to dampen our curiosity with the assurance, "La nuit, tous les chats son gris." She was mistaken.

RENDEZ-VOUS

"...how animated inanimate things can seem!..."

Peeping over the edge of the swimming pool with my chin on the hot terracotta tiles, I looked at the valley spread out below me. Layer upon layer of different shades of mauve punctuated by black, pencil-thin cypress trees.

Nearer to hand, a pair of very friendly chairs. How animated inanimate things can seem! Spectacles, sunhat and sandals -- blue shirt, belt and book, left to their own devices, while their owners are otherwise engaged.

Splash, splash! My ankles are grasped. I'm pulled downwards under the water by a creature far larger and stronger than me. Splash, splash! Cold wet lips meet hot moist tongues. Delicious, like Baked Alaska. I try to imagine drowning. My life starts to flash past me in reverse. Drowning must take an unconscionably long time. I break surface after covering only the last three days.

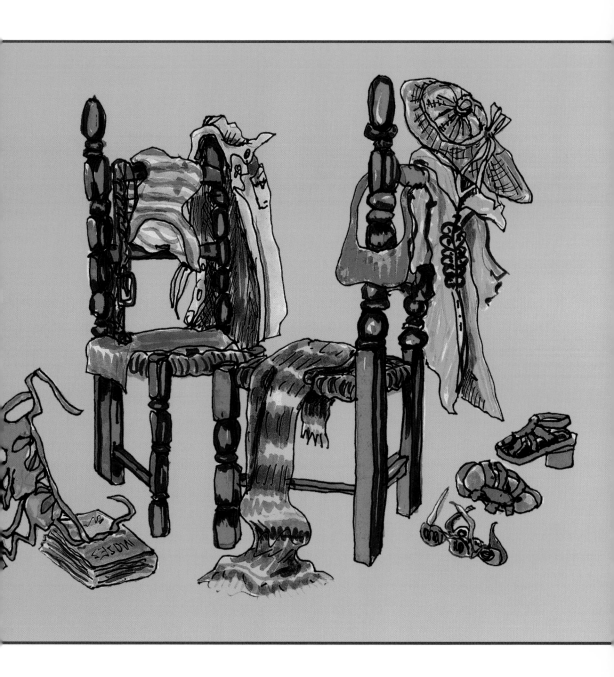

FOR BETTER FOR WORSE

"...and Tony, oblivious behind his newspaper..."

Nanny makes the house a home, and her day off, which she hardly ever takes, is a bleak day. I never realized until Nanny went away how much work she did. Usually she gets her sister to fill in for her, but this time they both had to go to their mother's funeral. It was only for a few days, but I felt as if I had a limb missing. I was also feeling a little flat after my Tuscan tryst. What Tony would have called a dirty weekend was, to me, a magical memory.

Sleepy-eyed, I would make breakfast in the kitchen. Getting the sausages and eggs on the table, and Melissa and Rupert into their uniforms in the right order drove me frantic. And Tony, oblivious behind his newspaper, didn't help. I thought he would agree to take the children to their schools, but he said not to rely on him as his new secretary was scheduling business breakfasts with American bankers in their hotels. So, with a Mac thrown over my nightie, I'd jump in the Mini, drop off the children, return home and get back into bed with my coffee and the telephone.

There are other things, too, that make a house a home, things you'd never notice 'til they're missing. Every evening Nanny goes through the whole house, drawing the curtains and turning on all the lamps. She puts ice in the drinks cabinet before Tony comes home, and cuts a few pieces of lemon rind for his martini. Of course, I always go out and buy the flowers and arrange them, but she tops up the flower vases and waters the plants. And when we come to bed at night, we always find our bed turned down with pyjamas and nightie laid out invitingly.

So this is what it's like to be a housewife -- I really am very lucky. I looked up "wife" in the Oxford Dictionary. I was disgusted with the entry: *Woman of low employment, hence fishwife, midwife and, in certain cases, housewife.*

CORNFLAKES

"...it's awful being a child. Grownups have absolute power..."

The Children miss Nanny, too. Especially Rupert. He's pining. He won't let me brush his hair and wouldn't finish his cornflakes this morning. When he doesn't know I'm watching, I catch him looking quite disconsolate. It's awful being a child. Grownups have absolute power. No wonder the children take it out on their parents later when they're teenagers.

There's an awful lot to do, which doesn't seem to amount to much -- just keeping things running. The "dear ones" are off at school and office, and I'm stuck at home doing general chores, until, bubbling with life and enthusiasm from their day in the outside world, they return with their demands.

ARBOR EROTICA

"...I looked out of the window into the back garden and saw Fantasia-like shapes in the gnarled old tree..."

LIFT OFF

"...the laundry basket came to earth with a terrible bump..."

Nanny's back. Thank Goodness! I celebrated by going on an adventure with John. He is so original. He took me to a ballooning event at Cirencester Park. I thought we'd be just watching but, at the last minute, there was room for two more in the Nimbus, and we clambered into this fragile-looking wicker laundry basket. Our pilot said he was an instructor, so 'not to worry'.

Lift Off was very gentle at a forty-five degree angle. We floated over the upturned faces of a wedding party, and a field of cows grazing peacefully until the roar of the 'burn' -- a large Bunsen Burner blowing hot air into the balloon -- sent them careering around in all directions, no doubt churning their milk to butter.

It was so beautiful, and exhilarating, until I started to think of the enormity of what I was doing. What would happen to the children if I should die. John put his arm around me but I found myself wishing it was Tony's.

The Instructor didn't let the air out right so the laundry basket came to earth with a terrible bump, dragging on its side for twenty yards or so. I was flattened underneath three male bodies, all the air squeezed out of my lungs. Not a good landing but, nonetheless, a very welcome one.

THE RISING SUN

"...the Rising Sun and the Union Jack
fluttering merrily together..."

Aunt Pauline was in the London Clinic having her varicose veins done, and
Cousin Felicity was off in Mustique. So, Uncle Freddie took me to Buckingham
Palace to a Garden Party celebrating the State Visit of the Emperor of Japan.

It was a glorious, sunny day. We followed the route the Queen had taken with the
Emperor earlier, in the open carriage from Victoria Station. The Rising Sun and
the Union Jack fluttering merrily together, lined the Mall from Trafalgar Square to
the Victoria Memorial. But, as we drove up in the official Austin Princess, Uncle
Freddie, looking behind him, pointed out the uncompromising brick tower,
peeping over the flags and trees -- an ominous reminder of Wartime London.

UNCLE FREDDIE

"...but 'forget' was what was being asked of us..."

Inside the Palace gardens, you could feel the undercurrent. Apart from pacifists, any man over forty-five, including our host, Prince Philip, was bound to have been in the War. This was the first time the "enemy" had set foot in our land. LEST WE FORGET is inscribed on all the war memorials, but 'forget' was what was being asked of us.

Uncle Freddie had spent two years in solitary confinement in the Far East, where he was tortured with dripping water. When we were presented to the Guest of Honour, Uncle Freddie gave the merest of bows and immediately moved on, leaving me stuck with the Emperor God. In that split second, mentally, I tried out opening gambits: "Is this your first visit to our country?" "Have you seen 'Hiroshima, Mon Amour'?" What had I ever heard about Japan beyond Green Tea, Geisha Girls and Inflatable Dolls? Botany! I remembered. The Emperor's a botanist. That's what he likes!

I reached into the heart-shaped neckline of my chiffon dress and drew out the perfect yellow rose I'd pinched from the Square Gardens. I bent over and popped it into the buttonhole of the small gentleman's black morning coat. Then,with a deep curtsey, I was far across the lawn, in search of Uncle Freddie.

The next morning, given pride of place on my breakfast tray, was Nanny's Daily Express, opened at the William Hickey column. An out-of-date photograph of me under the caption, "Say it with Flowers", accompanied a garbled version of my encounter with the Emperor God.

LOYAL SUBJECTS

"...I'll make you a nice cup of tea..."

I was at the Opening of Parliament with Uncle Freddie and Aunt Pauline, once more taking Felicity's place. While Aunt Pauline and I were looking down from the Visitors' Gallery, at elderly Lords in ermine-trimmed robes and their Ladies in full evening dress and tiaras -- all at 10.30 in the morning, a much more exciting event was taking place outside our own house.

A lot of anti-foxhunting demonstrators had lined up between the Royal Mews and the Palace, extending down both the Mall and Birdcage Walk, presumably hoping to impede the Queen's progress to the Houses of Parliament. Well, as I heard later, the Queen got to the Mews via internal passageways inside Buck House, got into her carriage and went the other way to avoid the fuss. This brought the whole entourage up Buckingham Palace Road, into Ebury Street -- right into our street!

Furious at being tricked, the demonstrators had come up both ends of Eaton Terrace. The Police from the Gerald Road Station, while waiting for tear gas, were hosing the angry men and women down with water. Meanwhile, three Royal Carriages were completely stuck in front of Lord Standish's house, right next door to us. Knowing that he and Lady Standish would be in Parliament, too, Nanny, as usual rising to the occasion, brushed aside the young policeman holding the lead horse of the Queen's carriage, and popped her nose through the ornate window.

"You can't wait out here in the cold, Your Majesty. Do come inside our house for 'elevenses'. I'll make you a nice cup of tea while you wait for those hooligans to be sent packing." So it was that the Monarch, sitting at the check lino table in our kitchen, had eggs and bacon with the plumber and Mrs. H. -- while Nanny held court.

MR. CORNICE

"...he opened 'consulting rooms' in his flat in Eaton Square..."

I'm over the moon! Mr. Cornice has offered me a part-time job in his decorating business. Nothing too strenuous -- I can fit it in between shopping for dresses and lunching with my girlfriends, whenever I like. He's even offered to open an account for me at San Lorenzo -- says it's good for business -- spreading the word. Of course he's hardly paying me anything to begin with. £20 a week. Mother calls it pin money.

I've always thought Mr. Cornice was just a little jealous of David Hicks and Michael Inchbald because, while equally talented, he was not, for other reasons, quite in their league. They had both gone to the 'right' schools and had married the 'right' women.

Ronald May (aliases: Mr. Cornice and Queen of the May), born early 1930's somewhere in Suburbia, had arrived by a circuitous route. After Grammar school in Pinner, and National Service as a private in the Royal Army Pay Corps, he got a job in the china department at The General Trading Company. Then, with backing from a mystery benefactor, he set up shop on the smart side of Beauchamp Place, with a well-built Dane called Bjorn. At first, he was known as the Great Dane, but after Mother, with her talent for puns, christened him Bjorn the Fringe, no-one ever called him anything else. Mr. Cornice took it a step further and sent out a newsletter called "Fringe Benefits."

This was the first time Mr. Cornice had openly lived with anyone. He let it be known that he only expected to receive invitations that included Bjorn. This caused consternation in the seating arrangements of some of the leading hostesses. Way ahead of Osborne & Little, Mr. Cornice started the fashion for putting elaborate patterned borders instead of cornices on plain or patterned wallpaper. The Word became flesh -- his nickname had preceded him.

Inevitably, Mr. Cornice broke up with The Fringe, whose chief observable
talent was marbleizing. The Fringe kept the shop, and Mr. Cornice, the mystery
benefactor. He opened 'consulting rooms' in his flat in Eaton Square. More time
for my 'patients,' he would say. To spite The Fringe, Mr. Cornice announced to
everyone that faux marbre was out and dragging (dragged paint) was in.

At this time, Mother, who considered she had discovered Mr. Cornice, confided in
me that she thought he was 'on something'. She had gone round to look at
patterns for her bedroom curtains, and found him, feet up on the purple sofa, a
brightly coloured cocktail in hand, mumbling about double vision, pink elephants,
and LSD. "Pounds, shillings and pence!" she protested. "You can't be short of
money, not with what you're charging me for the silk taffeta." Her eyes widened
when I explained that LSD was to his generation what Martinis were to hers.

SLOANE SQUARE

"...the Princes insisted on fresh flowers..."

Within days of starting work with Mr. Cornice I scored a bullseye. I introduced him to the Arab Princes we'd played Monopoly with. They'd got three adjoining houses in Queensgate, which needed an instant facelift. I was put on the job of installing everything from sideboards to soap dishes. I decided to get everything in one area -- I simply didn't have time to browse. Money was no object. I am now terribly popular with the antique dealers in Kensington Church Street.
I was also very popular with the flower man in Sloane Square. The Princes

insisted on fresh flowers -- every day. I would fill the Mini with exotic new blooms each morning, returning to Eaton Terrace in the evenng with a cargo of 'dead' plantlife.

I needed no sleep, I was up at six o'clock and didn't get home until after seven. I cancelled all dinners at our house and let Tony go out to parties as a grass widower, while I sat in the drawing room with pattern books and curtain materials strewn over sofa and chairs. Nanny was wonderful -- said it was like the wartime. She coped with all the housekeeping and took the children off my hands. Her nephew put his taxi at her disposal -- to do the school run, driving being one of my few indispensable roles in the household. I was so happy! I hadn't felt so alive since playing Joan of Arc in the school play -- except for Tuscany -- and the first months of marriage with Tony.

For a ten day period I rented my own furniture van to ferry things back and forth -- all on approval. Every morning I would round up the 'candidates' -- triple services of china and glass, rugs, lamps, bookshelves complete with leather bound books, everything including the kitchen sink. Each afternoon at four o'clock, the younger prince would meet me at Queensgate to make his selections. Two out-of-work dockers were on hand full time, to lug the heavy stuff around, and Mother's Mrs. H. came daily to dust, so the Prince's flowing robes wouldn't get soiled as he swept through the rooms like a beautiful white vulture. Much more knowledgeable, even than Mr. Cornice, he would turn Hepplewhite chairs upside down, searching for signatures.

The embossed wallpaper the Prince chose was so expensive, Mr. Cornice said it would've been cheaper to use pound notes!

I got paid, too. Mr. Cornice promised me five per cent of his profit, which at first I thought was a bit mean. But three weeks later, my take was two hundred and eighty crisp ten pound notes. Tony was amazed when I brought it home, loose in a Harrods shopping bag. Nanny was convinced I'd robbed the bank.

TONY'S CLOTHES

"...I found everything ticketyboo at Eaton Terrace..."

I'm back from Paris. Mr. Cornice sent me on a mission -- another shopping spree for the Arabs. John had wanted to come with me, but for some reason I was reluctant to mix pleasure with business. I really was excited by the job and I felt rather daring to be abroad on my own. A week at the Crillon passed pretty pleasantly.

On returning home, I found everything ticketyboo at Eaton Terrace. The flowers in the garden deadheaded, spring cleaning finished -- even the net curtains washed. In my absence, Nanny had taken to treating Tony as one of the children, even to the extent of laying out his clothes for him, while he had breakfast with the children in his dressing gown. "Good Lord, he'll never lift a finger for himself after this," I smiled to myself as, peeping into his dressingroom, I saw his blue suit, still with yesterday's Evening Standard in the pocket -- Nanny doesn't touch anything, throw anything out without permission. That she would leave for Tony to do. Clean home-ironed shirt and socks were laid over the arm of the red wicker chair.

"Hello?" I said, spying the packet of gold cut Benson & Hedges and the cigarette lighter lying on the non-U 'Y' fronts he insists on wearing. "Since when did Tony start smoking?"

DEAR JOHN

"...it's easier to tell you what I don't want..."

"Dear John,
I know I'm an absolute moral coward but I can't bear the thought of seeing your
disappointed face when I tell you..." Why is this so difficult? I am grateful to
John. I've found out so much about myself in the last few months since knowing
him. He's been a catalyst for me. Like a tin opener, he's dug out the sardines that
were imprisoned inside. I feel awful even thinking it, I'm finding him a bit clingy.

"You were so important to me -- were -- but one can't live on ecstasy. I'm
beginning to understand what I want -- and that if I don't get what I want I'll be
unhappy. I could pretend to be unselfish but that wouldn't work in the long run.
What I want is: to be me with a big ME. I want to be the hub of my own wheel.
It's easier to tell you what I don't want. I don't want to be only a WIFE, only a
MOTHER, only a LOVER, only a DAUGHTER, only a DINNER PARTY GIVER,
although I want to be all those things at the same time, and from time to time.
I think what I'm trying to tell you is that I don't want to be tied down to
ANYTHING now when I am just beginning to feel free. I thought WE represented
a new-found freedom, but you ve got too keen and want me to divorce Tony and
marry you. Of course if you'd left me after a one-night-stand, I'd be the one
waiting by the telephone, and crying my eyes out. So I am terribly grateful. Your
love for ME has freed me from loving YOU. Oh dear!"

Another thing, since I am not planning on living the rest of my life through
another person, albeit a gorgeous man, I'm looking at Tony with new eyes.
He is my husband, the father of my children. Many of my girlfriends, Philippa
in particular, would give their eye teeth to be married to him. I could hardly do
better, as Mother would say.

I put the finished letter in the envelope, licked the gum, and smoothed the flap down. I sealed it with a loving kiss and was surprised to find myself positively skipping down the street to the pillar box.

FINESSE

"...it must be hell, being in love with a married man..."

Tony doesn't know I know -- about him and his secretary. She brought some papers over to Eaton Terrace for Tony to sign, and he insisted she stay for dinner. "Your Mother's coming and Amanda can make up a 'four' for Bridge." She's not the little blond bird type I'd have thought Tony would have gone for as a "side dish". In another situation I might really rather like her.

Amanda drew me as a partner and seemed a little nervous. I know I would be. She's actually very pretty when she smiles but, when caught off guard, she has a worried, almost distraught, look. It must be hell, being in love with a married man who's also your boss -- all your eggs in one basket. She was debating whether to finesse Tony's Queen when the strain became too great. She put her cards face down on the table and took out a packet of Benson & Hedges, lighting a cigarette for herself with a trembling hand. It was then that I knew for sure.

Mother, who I hated to let in on this, but she does sometimes save me from myself -- advised "Turn a blind eye. Ask Tony for a fur, a string of pearls." Even though I was not exactly a saint, myself, I had only once gone the whole hog. Illogically, I felt miserable that Tony would betray me.

It's not really 'me' to be devious, but I decided to test him. "Tony, I would adore a new fur coat. My old fox looks as if it's been dragged through a hedge backwards. Shall I get a marmot or a racoon? Or should I have it refurbished?" I said, laughing weakly at my own joke.

"A mink, my wife deserves nothing less," he cried in very good humour, drawing me into his arms. "Aunt Pauline has a lovely coat. Get her to help you choose one at Harrods." The new mink is fabulous, but I feel a little sad when I wear it.

INFIDELITY

"...he should be paying me twenty quid an hour!...

Tony was amazingly cool when I finally confronted him with the 'evidence' about him and Amanda. "I love you, Penelope. Let's face it, you're the best person for me to be married to. We have a good life, lovely children, nothing need change." I pretended to rearrange the tulips on the sofa table, and let him run on.

"Honestly, Pen," said Tony. "I'll overlook it if you have a little fling on the side, yourself. Maybe John -- or that friend of your brother's who plays Racquets with him at Queens. He's rather a decent looking chap" This was too much! Not only was my husband giving me 'permission' to take a lover -- he also wanted to 'choose' him! I threw the bowl of flowers into his lap, not caring about Mr. Cornice's raw silk chair cover.

At my next session with Dr. Tryon, I naturally didn't confide in him my dream about 'his' transference, but I did consult him about Tony's affair. Dr. Tryon, in his comforting voice, explained: "For most people, whether they care to admit it or not, occasional infidelity is a tonic for both body and soul. Of course, infidelity must be in the right proportion to fidelity -- a rare treat. Overdo it and it loses its bite." I was astonished by his attitude and wondered if it was Sigmund Freud or Noel Coward, who had been feeding him his lines.

He wanted me to give him the lowdown on my affair with John, but I was "over" that. And he seemed unduly fascinated by Aunt Pauline's house near Lucca -- the furnishings, number of bedrooms, size of the pool, was it ever for rent? He even got a map out and made me show him its exact position in relation to Florence.

The incredible thing was, when I finally got Dr. Tryon to concentrate on what I was interested in, he seemed more concerned with why I had thrown the flowers on Tony's lap, rather than with Tony's behaviour with Amanda. He explained to me that he didn't care about Tony's feelings, but only about mine. He asked me whether I had ever looked deeply into the centre of a tulip, and if that had ever made me feel sexy. I have a strong suspicion Dr. Tryon is deriving vicarious pleasure at my expense. He should be paying me twenty quid an hour!

BATHTIME

*"...I spent the time giving myself a hair rinse --
flaming chestnut..."*

Tony and I didn't go to bed at all last night. He came home from work late,
having spent three hours with Patrick at the bar of the Cavalry Club. I spent the
time giving myself a face mask and a hair rinse -- flaming chestnut. It looked
fantastic, but it didn't lift my spirits. At nine o'clock, I finally had a tray of boiled
eggs and toast in Nanny's room, watching Telly with her.

I was in the bath, reading about Sarah Bernhardt's extraordinary life and, by
comparison, feeling mine definitely left something to be desired, when Tony
burst in, demanding I put on a nightie and join him in the study, as he had
"something to tell me".

I was not best pleased at this intrusion as, since the Amanda discussion, I had
put Tony in Coventry and had been keeping myself to myself. After a couple of
nights of trying to sleep with a row of pillows between us, I had moved all the
things from my side of the bed onto the campaign chest in his dressing room.
To make room for them, I'd swept all his stuff -- silver framed photographs of
his mother and father, cufflinks and studs, ivory hairbrushes -- the lot -- into the
bottom drawer to bed down amongst his rarely used cummerbunds and
embroidered Eton waistcoats.

Being the man, he should have slept in the little bed, himself, but he'd refused
point blank to leave the marital bed.

IN VINO VERITAS

"...it's no good arguing with someone who's plastered..."

I decided not to have a row with him. It's no good arguing with someone who's plastered. You end up shouting and acting as badly, yourself. I poured myself a strong gin and tonic and forced myself to sit patiently in the wing chair to hear what he had to tell me. Tony wouldn't look at me. He sat clutching his whisky, an arm draped over the back of the sofa. He looked dreadful -- bags under his eyes and hair in a mess. He kept repeating that he loved me but that he'd been keeping a secret from me. Now he had to tell me. "Why, now, then?," I asked, steeling myself for some horror worse than his affair with Amanda. What could be worse? Unless he had herpes, or cancer, or something?

"Because you have to know. You will know anyway." Tony helped himself to another glass of whisky. He started pacing around the room, which drives me mad. He was speaking with his back to me so I couldn't see his face. He tied himself up in knots with his legs crossed about three times and his arm wound around his neck like Isadora Duncan's scarf. "I've lost our money -- quite a lot of it. The market... I got the bank involved in a sort of pyramid... you wouldn't understand the details... my syndicate at Lloyds, too, has been disastrous this year..." he was sobbing. I knew the market was down, but it couldn't be that bad.

VERITAS IN VINO

"...was this shivering creature the Master of the House?..."

We may have to sell the house. "We'll have to let Nanny go," he groaned.

"Noooooooh! Never! I'm sure Mother will pay Nanny's wages -- until we can again," I said, putting my arms around him to try and comfort him. He hurled me violently away from him, sending me reeling into the drinks cabinet. He paid no attention to the falling bottles and glasses but started a moaning that reminded me of bagpipes at a Scottish funeral. "Tony!" My tone forced him to look at me. "Not Mother's money, too?" He looked away.

I took a deep breath. "Oh, God, you poor thing! How will you ever break it to Mother? Oh, you want *me* to? Throughout our marriage, even in the difficult times, I had always looked up to Tony -- as the man, as the person ultimately in charge. Like "She" in the Rider Haggard book, Tony had undergone a transformation. Was this shivering creature the Master of the House?

Right, Tony," I said. "I'll deal with it -- on condition that you sack your precious secretary and you never have secrets from me ever again." Tony collapsed on the sofa, and I went upstairs to talk to Nanny, who was already up and about, making her early morning tea. I felt a new sense of power I'd not had before.

THE BLUE ROLLS

*"...in three months I would earn more
than he gets in a whole year..."*

My whole life has been changed by a single telephone call! I'm not just over the moon, I'm in seventh heaven!

Mr. Cornice is to do up three royal palaces for our clients in the Gulf -- and, by special request of *my* Prince, I'm to do all the women's quarters -- the Seraglio. Eleven wives, thirty odd concubines, over a hundred children, nurses, teachers, and general hangers-on (not to mention the eunuchs) add up to many rolls of chintz. The bed linen, alone -- linen not cotton -- all monogrammed, would be no mean order.

I was bubbling over with plans for spending the money. Now, we needn't think of selling the house. Nanny could start getting paid again. But Tony was very quiet at dinner, the night I told him. Could he be jealous of me? In three months I would be earning more than he gets in a whole year -- considerably more than the Prime Minister, too.

John's been trying to get back with me. He wangled himself a trip to the Middle East, to take photographs for an article entitled "Architecture in the Sand". He wanted to go with me. Absolutely not! No way! I've quite lost interest in him. Fresh fields and pastures new -- if you can say that about the desert. Anyway, I've got a career now, that I'm really keen on, and I'm getting on better with Tony. Since the financial fiasco, he and I are on an equal footing.

Tony and I decided to say *goodbye* at Eaton Terrace, not at the airport, since the Prince was sending his blue Rolls to take me and Mr. Cornice right onto the runway. (We're going to *do* the plane, too - when we have time!). Mother gave me her signed first edition of *The Wilder Shores of Love*. The Bachelor, who's going to make her his fifth bride, handed me the latest polaroid camera, in an Hermes holdall with *Florence of Arabia* stamped on the leather trim.

"It's only for three weeks," I said, giving Tony a hug, and Melissa and Rupert tearful kisses. "Nanny will hold the fort while I'm gone."

LAST WORD

"...Penelope," said Nanny, "things will never be the same."